# The Cats have Come to Tea

## and other poems

Compiled by Tig Thomas

Miles Kelly

First published in 2010 by Miles Kelly Publishing Ltd
Harding's Barn, Bardfield End Green, Thaxted, Essex, CM6 3PX, UK

2 4 6 8 10 9 7 5 3 1

*Editorial Director* Belinda Gallagher

*Art Director* Jo Cowan

*Assistant Editor* Claire Philip

*Designer* Joe Jones

*Junior Designer* Kayleigh Allen

*Production Manager* Elizabeth Collins

*Reprographics* Stephan Davis, Ian Paulyn

ISBN 978-1-84810-368-9

Printed in China

British Library Cataloguing-in-Publication Data
A catalogue record for this book is available from the British Library

**ACKNOWLEDGEMENTS**

The publishers would like to thank Kirsten Wilson for
the illustrations she contributed to this book.

All other artwork from the Miles Kelly Artwork Bank

The publishers would like to thank Dariusz Gudowicz/Fotolia.com
for the use of their photograph (page 21)

Made with paper from a sustainable forest

www.mileskelly.net
info@mileskelly.net

**www.factsforprojects.com**

Self-publish your
children's book

buddingpress.co.uk

# Contents

# Planning

In summer when I go to bed,
The sun still streaming overhead,
My bed becomes so small and hot
With sheets and pillow in a knot,
And then I lie and try to see
The things I'd really like to be.

I think I'd be a glossy cat,
A little plump, but not too fat.
I'd never touch a bird or mouse,
I'm much too busy round the house.

And then a fierce and hungry hound,
The king of dogs for miles around;
I'd chase the postman just for fun
To see how quickly he could run.

Perhaps I'd be a crocodile
Within the marshes of the Nile,
And paddle in the river-bed
With dripping mud-caps on my head.

Or maybe next a mountain goat
With shaggy whiskers at my throat,
Leaping streams and jumping rocks
In stripey pink and purple socks.

Or else I'd be a polar bear
And on an iceberg make my lair;
I'd keep a shop in Baffin Sound
To sell icebergs by the pound.

And then I'd be a wise old frog
Squatting on a sunken log,
I'd teach the fishes lots of games
And how to read and write their names.

An Indian lion then I'd be
And lounge about on my settee;
I'd feed on nothing but bananas
And spend all day in my pyjamas.

I'd like to be a tall giraffe,
Making lots of people laugh,
I'd do a tap dance in the street
With little bells upon my feet.

And then I'd be a foxy fox
Streaking through the hollyhocks,
Horse or hound would ne'er catch me;
I'm a master of disguise, you see.

I think I'd be a chimpanzee
With musical ability,
I'd play a silver clarinet
Or form a Monkey String Quartet.

And then a snake with scales of gold
Guarding hoards of wealth untold,
No thief would dare to steal a pin –
But friends of mine I would let in.

But then before I really know
Just what I'd be or where I'd go,
My bed becomes so wide and deep
And all my thoughts are fast asleep.

*Thomas Hood*

# The Cats have Come to Tea

What did she see – oh, what did she see,
As she stood leaning against the tree?
Why all the Cats had come to tea.

What a fine turn out – from
    round about,
All the houses had let
    them out,
And here they were with
    scamper and shout.

"Mew–mew–mew!" was all they could say,
    And, "We hope we find you well today."

Mew-mew-mew!

**Mew-mew-mew!**

Oh, what should she do –
  oh, what should she do?
What a lot of milk they would get through;
For here they were with "Mew–mew–mew!"

She didn't know – oh, she didn't know,
If bread and butter they'd like or no;
They might want little mice, oh! oh! oh!
Dear me – oh, dear me,
All the cats had come to tea.

*Kate Greenaway*

Mew- mew-mew!

# Meet-on-the-Road

"Now, pray, where are you going, child?" said Meet-on-the-Road.

"To school, sir, to school, sir," said Child-as-It-Stood.

"What have you in your basket, child?" said Meet-on-the-Road.

"My dinner, sir, my dinner, sir," said Child-as-It-Stood.

"What have you for your dinner, child?" said Meet-on-the-Road.

"Some pudding, sir, some pudding, sir," said Child-as-It-Stood.

"Oh, then I pray, give me a share," said Meet-on-the-Road.

"I've little enough for myself, sir," said Child-as-It-Stood.

"What have you got that cloak on for?" said Meet-on-the Road.

"To keep the wind and cold from me," said Child-as-It-Stood.

"I wish the wind would blow through you," said Meet-on-the-Road.
"Oh, what a wish! Oh, what a wish!" said Child-as-It Stood.
"Pray what are those bells ringing for?" said Meet-on-the-Road.
"To ring bad spirits home again," said Child-as-It-Stood.
"Oh, then, I must be going, child!" said Meet-on-the-Road.
"So fare you well, so fare you well," said Child-as-It-Stood.

*Anonymous*

# Nonsense

I had a boat, and the boat had wings;
And I did dream that we went a flying
Over the heads of queens and kings,
Over the souls of dead and dying,
Up among the stars and the great white rings,
And where the Moon on her back is lying.

Mary Coleridge

# Once

Once I was a monarch's daughter,
And sat on a lady's knee;
But am now a nightly rover,
Banished to the ivy tree.

Crying **hoo, hoo, hoo, hoo, hoo, hoo,
Hoo, hoo, hoo,** My feet are cold.

Pity me, for here you see me
Persecuted, poor, and old.

I once was a king's daughter
And sat on my father's knee
But now I'm a poor hoolet
And hide in a hollow tree

*Anonymous*

# A Song for Scaring Goblins Away

One, two –
Hit and Hew!
Three, four –
Blast and bore!
Five, six –
There's a fix!
Seven, eight –
Hold it straight!
Nine, ten –
Hit again
Hurry! Scurry!
Bother! Smother!

There's a toad
In the road!
Smash it!
Squash it!
Fry it!
Dry it!
You're another!
Up and off!
There's enough – **Huuuuuh!**

*George Macdonald*

Curdie, the miner boy, sings this song in The Princess and the Goblin by George Macdonald to scare away the creepy, night-time goblins who lurk around the mine.

# Good Morning

The year's at the Spring,
And day's at the morn;
Morning's at seven;
The hillside's dew-pearled;
The lark's on the wing;
The snail's on the thorn;
God's in his heaven –
All's right with the world.

*Robert Browning*

# Three Little Rules

Three little rules we all should keep.
To make life happy and bright.

Smile in the morning, smile at noon.
And keep on smiling at night.

*Anonymous*

# Hair Brushing

One for a tangle,
One for a curl,
One for a boy
And one for a girl,
One to make a parting,
One to tie a bow,
One to blow the cobwebs out
And one to make it grow.

*Anonymous*

# From *Poem to her Daughter*

Daughter, take this amulet,

tie it with cord and caring.

I'll make you a chain of coral and pearl

to glow on your neck. I'll dress you nobly.

A gold clasp too – fine, without flaw,

to keep with you always.

When you bathe, sprinkle perfume, and
  weave your hair in braids,

string jasmine for the counterpane.

Wear your clothes like a bride,

anklets for your feet, bracelets for your arms. . .

Don't forget rosewater,

don't forget henna for the palms of your hands. . .

*Mwana Kupona binti Msham*

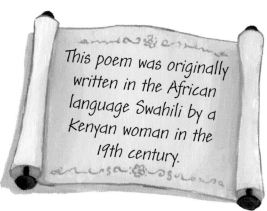

**Amulet** a charm to keep the wearer safe

**Counterpane** bedspread

**Henna** a reddish-brown dye

This poem was originally written in the African language Swahili by a Kenyan woman in the 19th century.

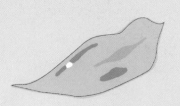

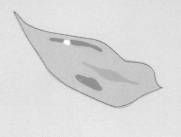

# A Kiss when I Wake

A kiss when I wake in the morning
A kiss when I go to bed,
A kiss when I burn my fingers,
A kiss when I bump my head.
A kiss when my bath begins
A kiss when my bath is over,
My mamma is as full of kisses
As nurse is full of pins.
A kiss when I play with my rattle;
A kiss when I pull her hair,
She covered me all over with kisses
The day that I fell down stair.
A kiss when I give her trouble,
A kiss when I give her joy;
There's nothing like mamma's kisses
To her own little baby boy.

*Anonymous*

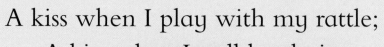
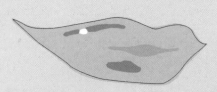

# The Hurt Hand

Pat it, kiss it,
Stroke it, bless it;
Three days' sunshine, three days' rain,
Little hand all well again.

*Anonymous*

# Baby Mine

Baby mine, over the trees;
Baby mine, over the flowers;
Baby mine, over the sunshine;
Baby mine, over the showers;

Baby mine, over the land;
Baby mine, over the water.
Oh, when had a mother before
Such a sweet – such a sweet, little daughter!

*Kate Greenaway*

# The Land of Story Books

At evening when the lamp is lit,
Around the fire my parents sit;
They sit at home and talk and sing,
And do not play at anything.

Now, with my little gun, I crawl
All in the dark along the wall,
And follow round the forest track
Away behind the sofa back.

There, in the night, where none can spy,
All in my hunter's camp I lie,
And play at books that I have read
Till it is time to go to bed.

These are the hills, these are the woods,
These are my starry solitudes;
And there the river by whose brink
The roaring lions come to drink.

I see the others far away
As if in firelit camp they lay,
And I, like to an Indian scout,
Around their party prowled about.

So, when my nurse comes in for me,
Home I return across the sea,
And go to bed with backward looks
At my dear land of story books.

Robert Louis Stevenson

Imagine a dark room lit only by a lamp. Behind the furniture would be a perfect place to pretend to be a hunter or explorer.

23

# Godfrey Gordon Gustavus Gore

Godfrey Gordon Gustavus Gore
Godfrey Gordon Gustavus Gore –
No doubt you have heard the name before –
Was a boy who never would shut a door!

The wind might whistle, the wind might roar,
And teeth be aching and throats be sore,
But still he never would shut the door.
His father would beg, his mother implore,
"Godfrey Gordon Gustavus Gore,
    We really do wish you would shut the door!"

Their hands they wrung, their hair they tore;
But Godfrey Gordon Gustavus Gore
Was deaf as the buoy out at the Nore.
When he walked forth the folks would roar,
"Godfrey Gordon Gustavus Gore,
    Why don't you think to shut the door?"

They rigged up a Shutter with sail and oar,
And threatened to pack off Gustavus Gore
On a voyage of penance to Singapore.

But he begged for mercy and said, "No more!
Pray do not send me to Singapore
On a Shutter, and then I will shut the door!"

"You will?" said his parents; "then keep on shore!
But mind you do! For the plague is sore
Of a fellow that never will shut the door,
Godfrey Gordon Gustavus Gore!"

*William Brighty Rands*

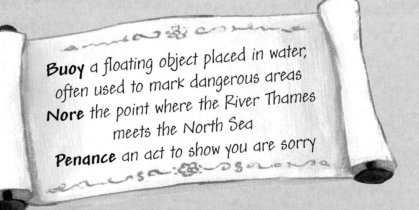

**Buoy** a floating object placed in water, often used to mark dangerous areas
**Nore** the point where the River Thames meets the North Sea
**Penance** an act to show you are sorry

# From *A Woman's Questions*

How old is God? Has he grey hair?
Can He see yet? Where did He have to stay
Before – you know – he had made – Anywhere?
Who does He pray to – when He has to pray?

How many drops are in the sea?
How many stars? – Well, then, you ought to know
How many flowers are on an apple tree?
How does the wind look when it doesn't blow?

Where does the rainbow end? And why
Did – Captain Kidd – bury the gold there? When
Will this world burn? And will the firemen try
To put the fire out with the engines then?

If you should ever die, may we
Have pumpkins growing in the garden, so
My fairy godmother can come for me,
When there's a prince's ball, and let me go?

*Sarah Morgan Bryan Piatt*

# The Dumb Soldier

When the grass was closely mown,
Walking on the lawn alone,
In the turf a hole I found,
And hid a soldier underground.

Spring and daisies came apace;
Grasses hide my hiding place;
Grasses run like a green sea
O'er the lawn up to my knee.

Under grass alone he lies,
Looking up with leaden eyes,
Scarlet coat and pointed gun,
To the stars and to the sun.

When the grass is ripe like grain,
When the scythe is stoned again,
When the lawn is shaven clear,
Then my hole shall reappear.

I shall find him, never fear,
I shall find my grenadier;
But for all that's gone and come,
I shall find my soldier dumb.

He has lived, a little thing,
In the grassy woods of spring;
Done, if he could tell me true,
Just as I should like to do.

Grenadier a type
of soldier

He has seen the starry hours
And the springing of the flowers;
And the fairy things that pass
In the forests of the grass.

In the silence he has heard
Talking bee and ladybird,
And the butterfly has flown
O'er him as he lay alone.

Not a word will he disclose,
Not a word of all he knows.
I must lay him on the shelf,
And make up the tale myself.

*Robert Louis Stevenson*

# A Birthday Song

Our darling Roberta,
No sorrow shall hurt her
If we can prevent it
Her whole life long.
Her birthday's our fete day,
We'll make it our great day,
And give her our presents
And sing her our song.
May pleasures attend her
And may the Fates send her
The happiest journey
Along her life's way.
With skies bright above her
And dear ones to love her!
Dear Bob! Many happy
Returns of the day!

*E Nesbit*

In The Railway Children, Roberta's mother writes this song for the family to sing on her 12th birthday.

# A Nursery Song

One cannot turn a minute,
But mischief there you're in it,
A-getting at my books, John,
With mighty bustling looks, John;
Or poking at the roses
In midst of which your nose is;
Or climbing on a table,
No matter how unstable,
And turning up your quaint eye
And half-shut teeth with 'Mayn't I?
Or else you're off at play, John,
Just as you'd be all day, John,
With hat or not, as happens,
And there you dance, and clap hands,
Or on the grass go rolling,
Or plucking flowers, or bowling,
And getting me expenses
With losing balls o'er fences;

And see what flow'rs the weather
Has render'd fit to gather;
And, when we home must jog, you
Shall ride my back, you rogue you.
Your hat adorn'd with fir-leaves,
Horse-chestnut, oak, and vine-leaves;
And so, with green o'erhead, John,
Shall whistle home to bed, John.
But see, the sun shines brightly;
Come, put your hat on rightly,
And we'll among the bushes,
And hear your friends the thrushes.

*Leigh Hunt*

# The Teacher

I'd like to be a teacher, and have a clever brain,
Calling out,

## "Attention, please!"
and

## "Must I speak in vain?"

I'd be quite strict with boys and girls whose minds
   I had to train,
And all the books and maps and things I'd carefully
   explain;
I'd make then learn the dates of kings,
   and all the capes of Spain;
But I wouldn't be a teacher if...

   I couldn't use the cane.

    Would you?

*C J Dennis*

# Quick, Quick

Quick, quick
The cat's been sick
Where, where?
Under the chair.
Hasten, hasten
Fetch a basin.
Too late, too late,
'Tis all in vain,
The cat has licked it
Up again.

*Anonymous*

# The Story of Johnny Head-in-Air

As he trudged along to school,
It was always Johnny's rule
To be looking at the sky
And the clouds that floated by;
But what just before him lay,
In his way,
Johnny never thought about;
So that everyone cried out,

**"Look at little Johnny there,
Little Johnny Head-in-Air!"**

Running just in Johnny's way
Came a little dog one day;
Johnny's eyes were still astray
Up on high,
In the sky;
And he never heard them cry

"**Johnny, mind, the dog is nigh!**"
**Bump!**
**Dump!**

Down they fell, with such a thump,
Dog and Johnny in a lump!

Once, with head as high as ever,
Johnny walked beside the river.
Johnny watched the swallows trying
Which was cleverest at flying.
Oh! What fun!
Johnny watched the bright round sun
Going in and coming out;

This was all he thought about.
So he strode on, only think!
To the river's very brink,
Where the bank was and steep,
And the water very deep;
And the fishes, in a row,
Stared to see him coming so.

One step more! Oh! Sad to tell!
Headlong in poor Johnny fell.
And the fishes, in dismay,
Wagged their tails and swam away.
There lay Johnny on his face,
With his nice red writing-case;
But, as they were passing by,
Two strong men had heard him cry;
And, with sticks, these two strong men
Hooked poor Johnny out again.

Oh! You should have seen him shiver
When they pulled him from the river.
He was in a sorry plight,

Dripping wet, and such a fright!
Wet all over, everywhere,
Clothes, and arms, and face, and hair:
Johnny never will forget
What it is to be so wet.

And the fishes, one, two, three,
Are come back again, you see;
Up they came the moment after,
To enjoy the fun and laughter.
Each popped out his little head,
And, to tease poor Johnny, said

## "Silly little Johnny, look, You have lost your writing-book!"

Heinrich Hoffmann

# Index of First Lines